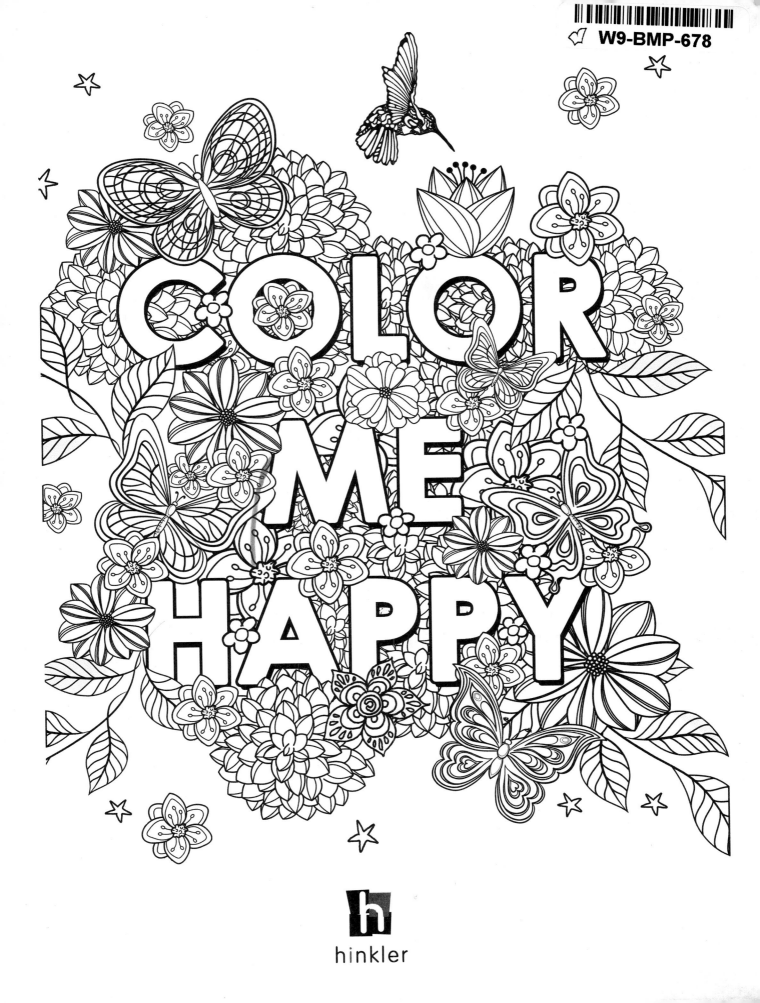

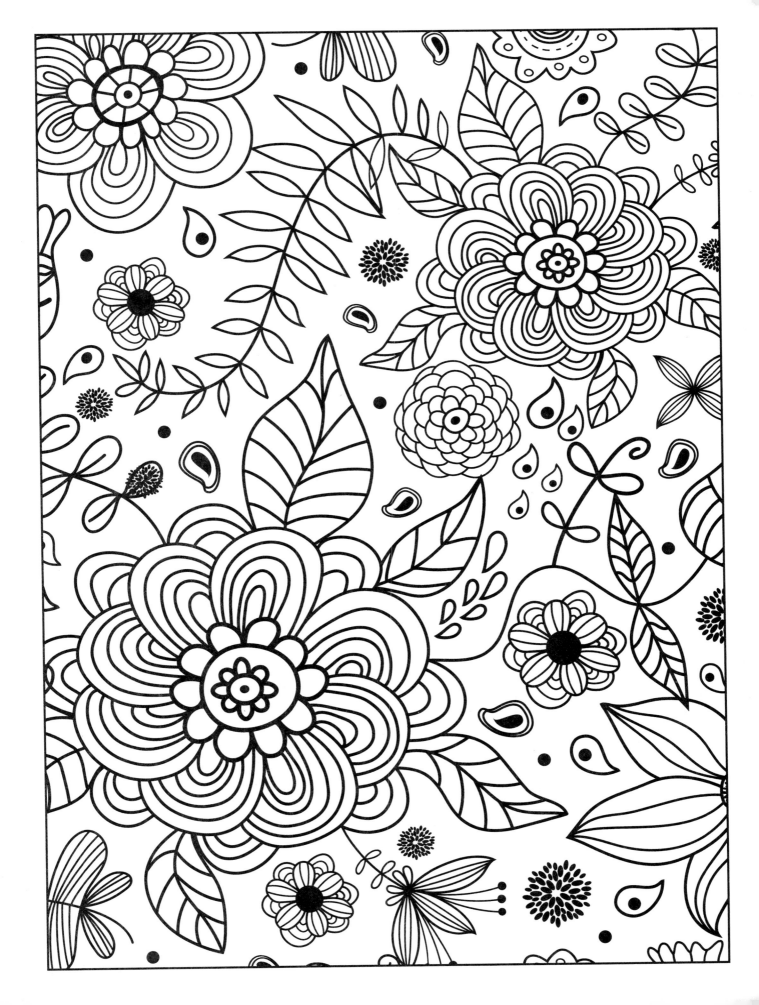

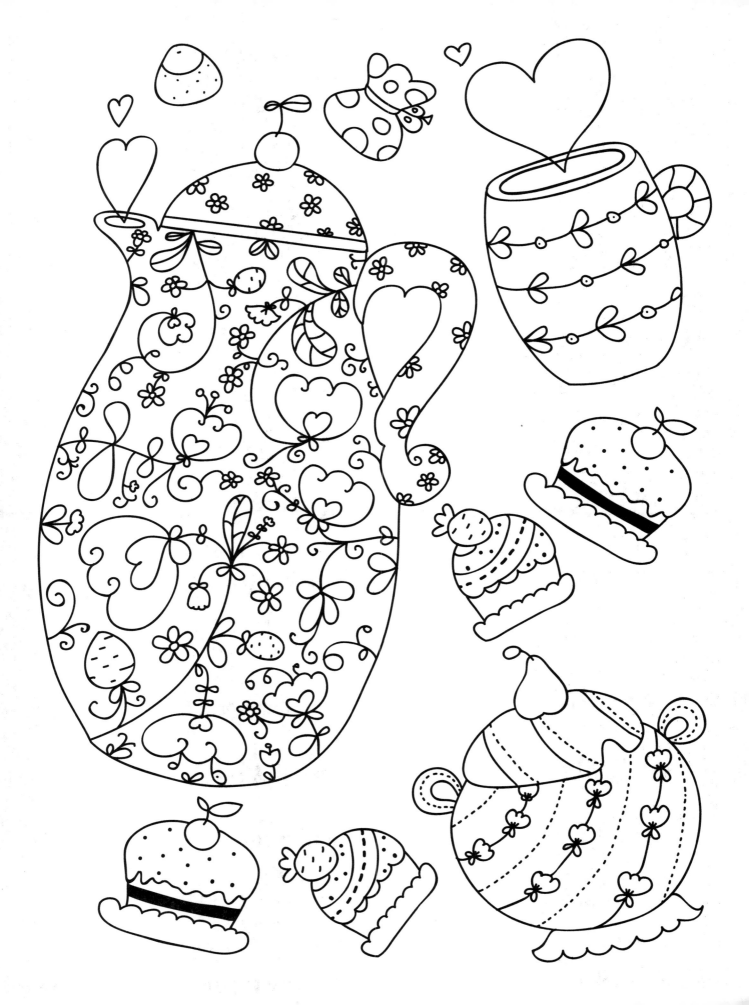

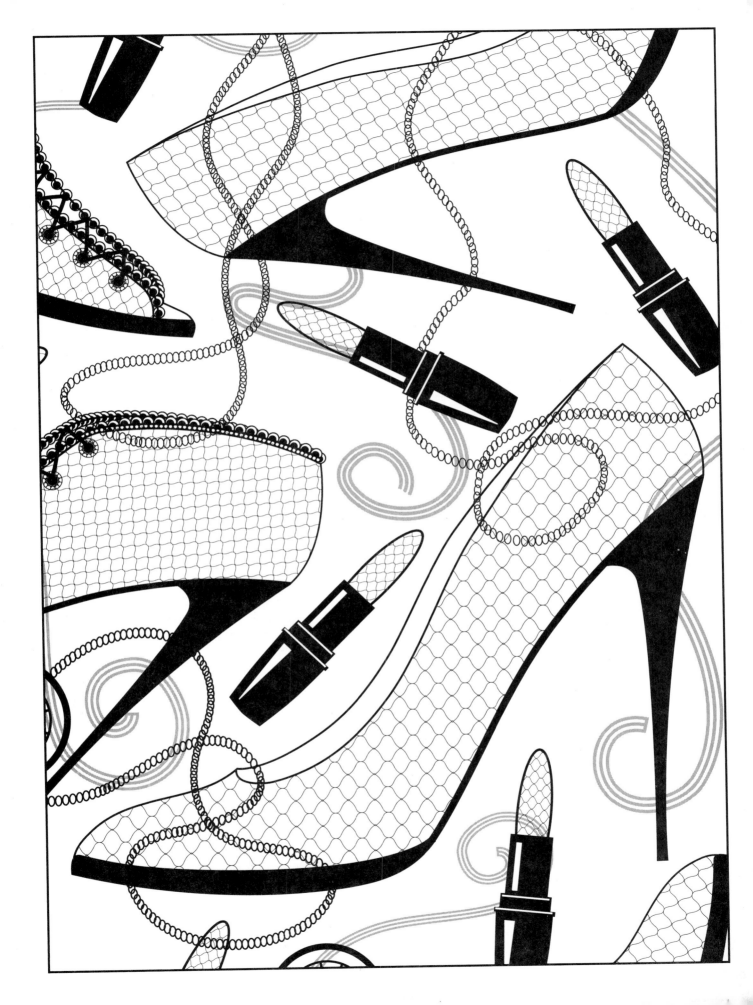

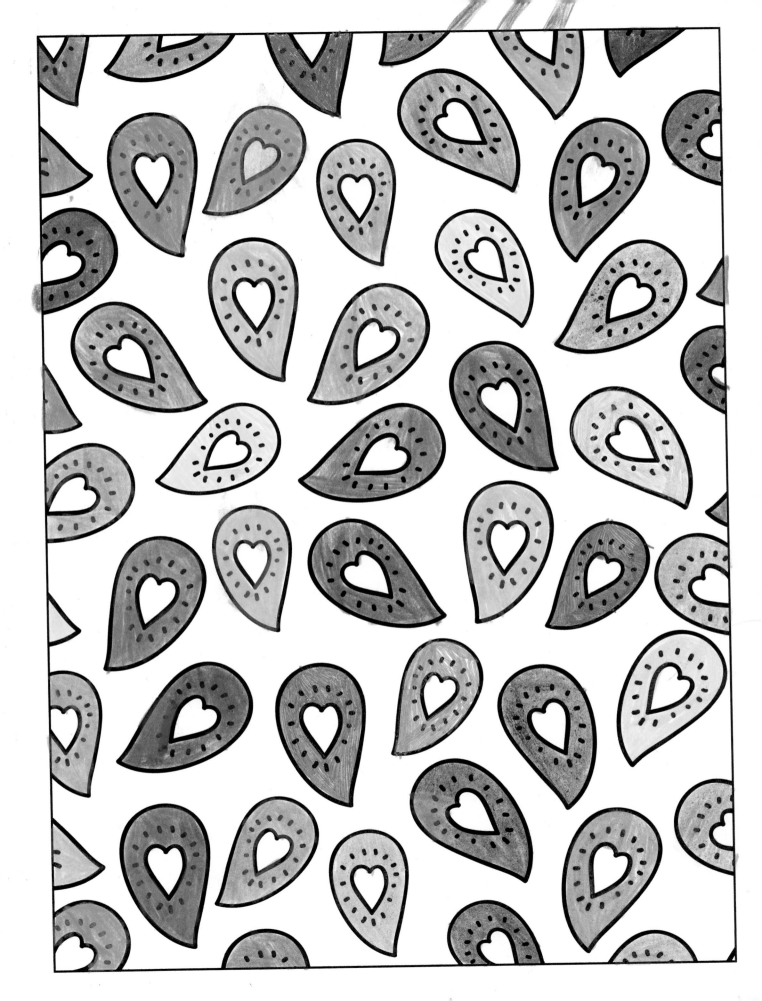

March 31st 2017
3rd grade
9 yrs old

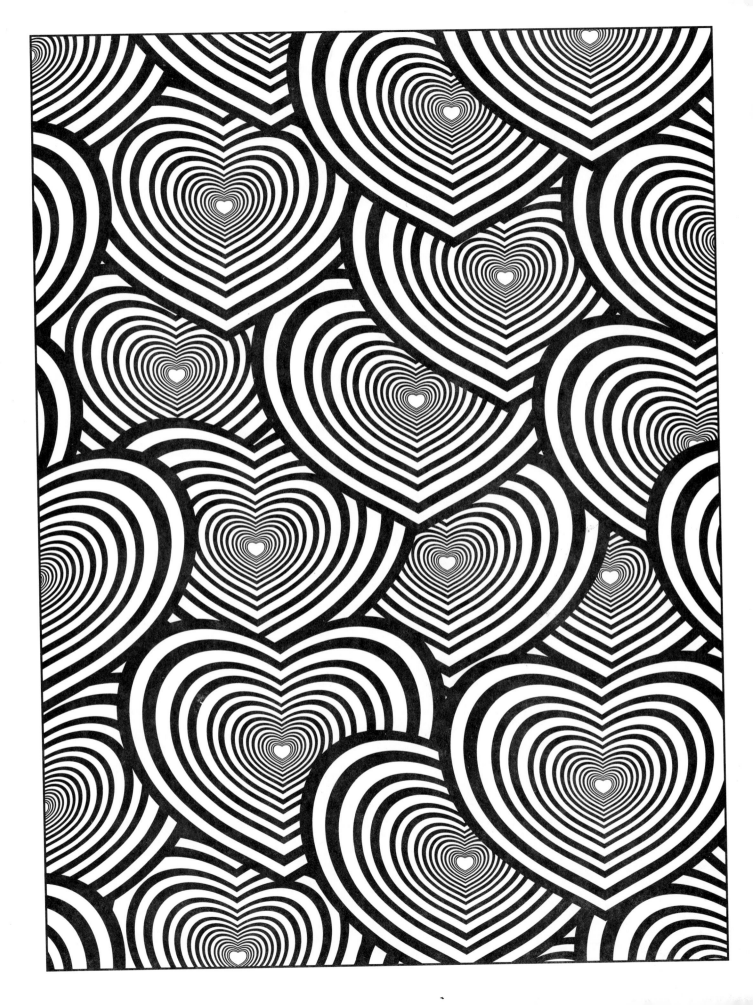

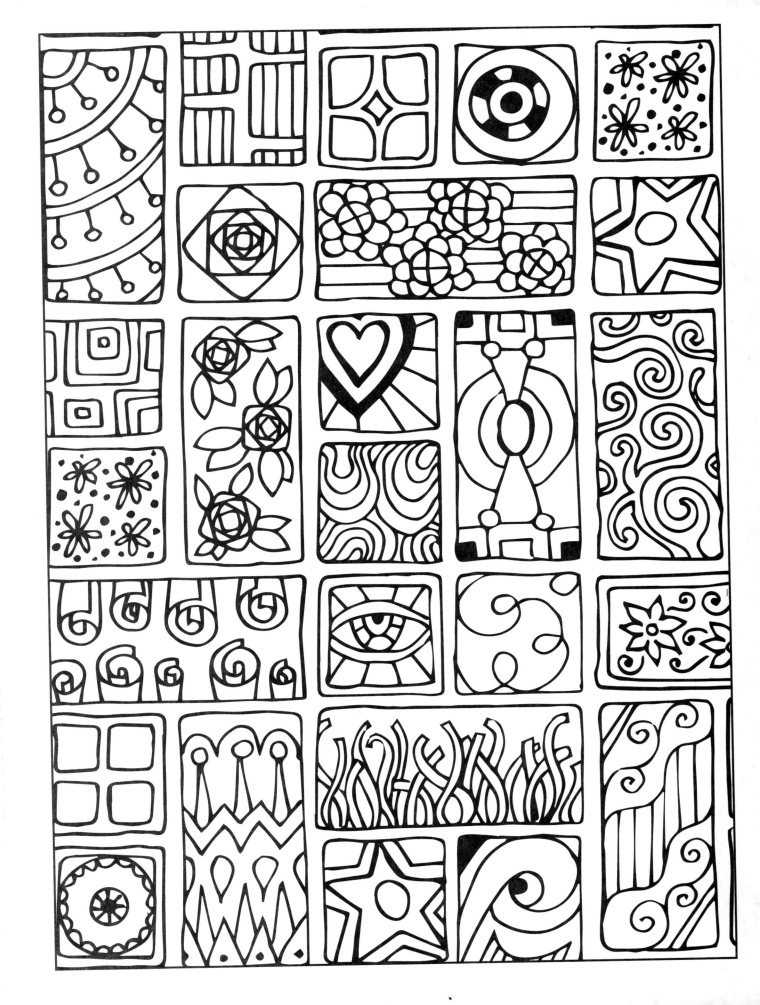

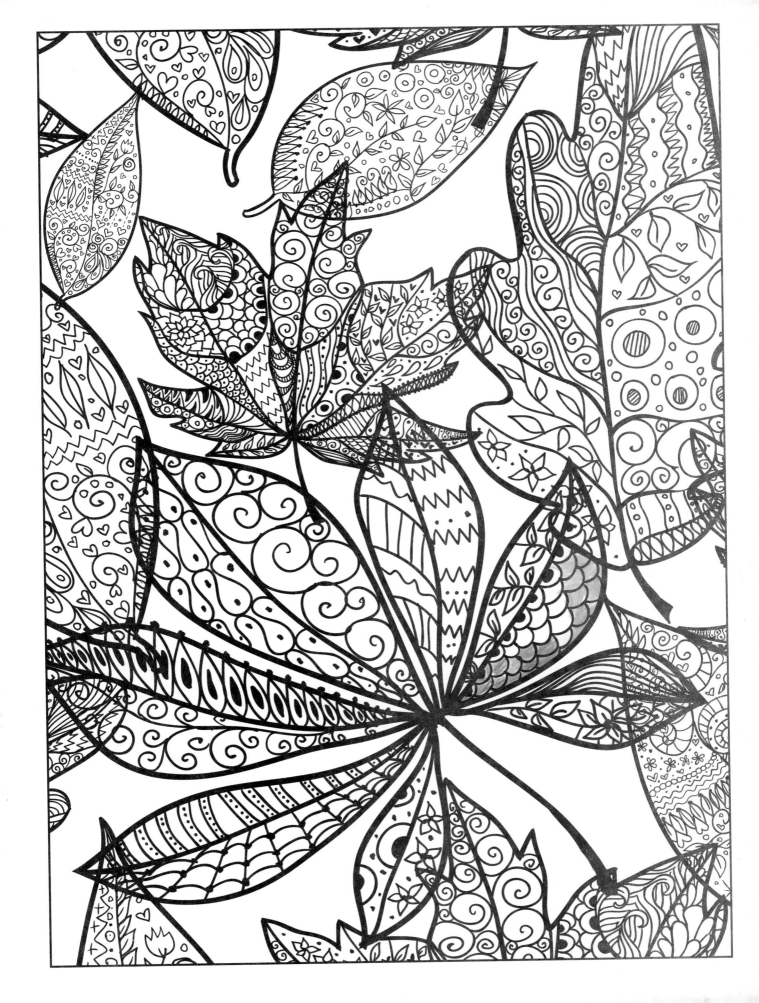

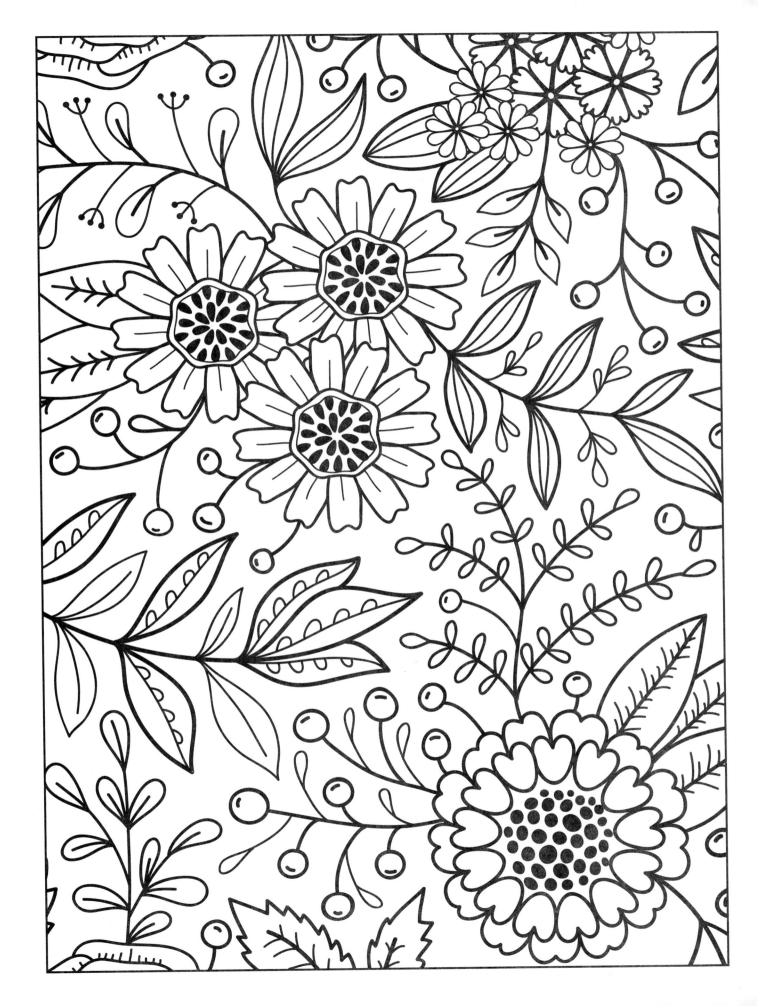

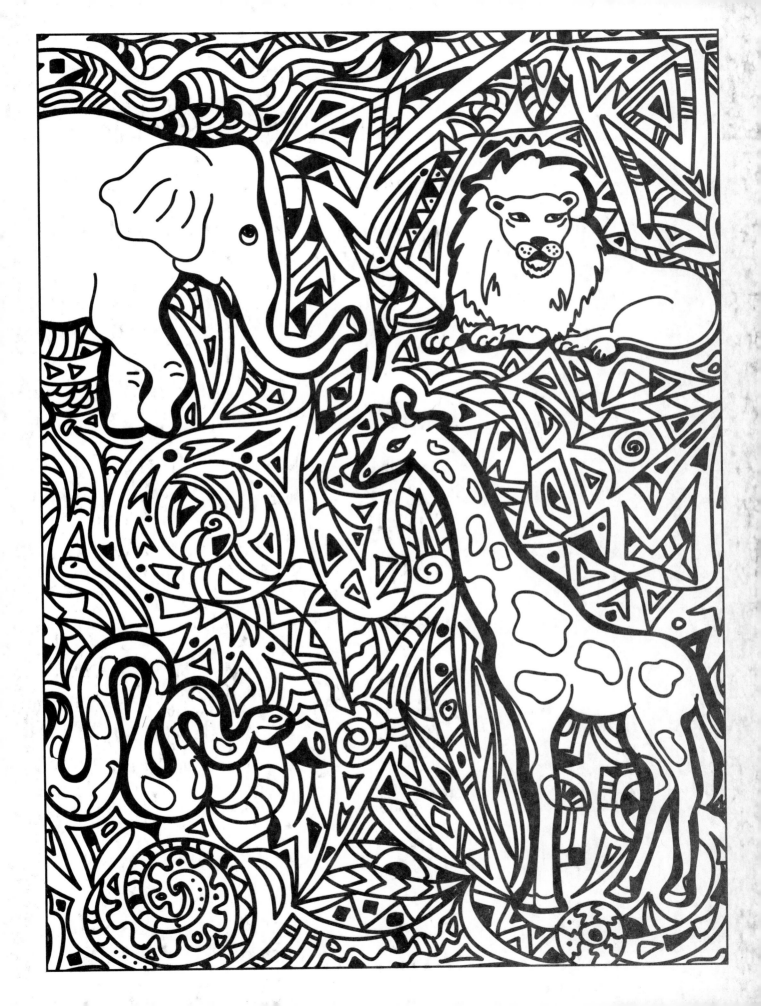

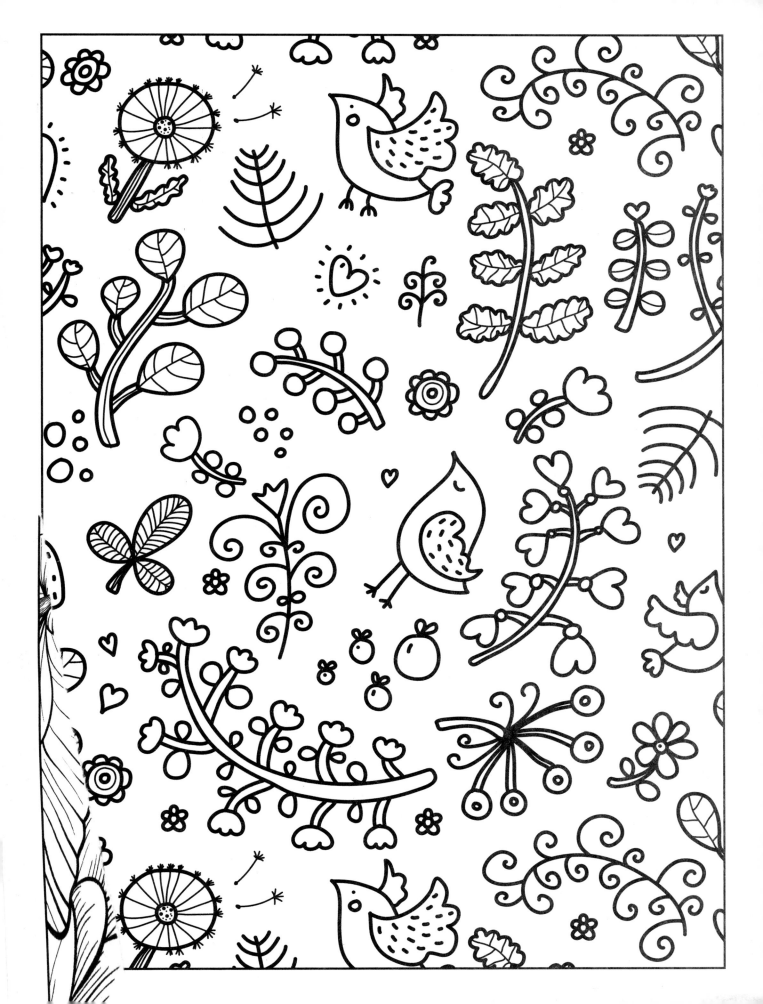

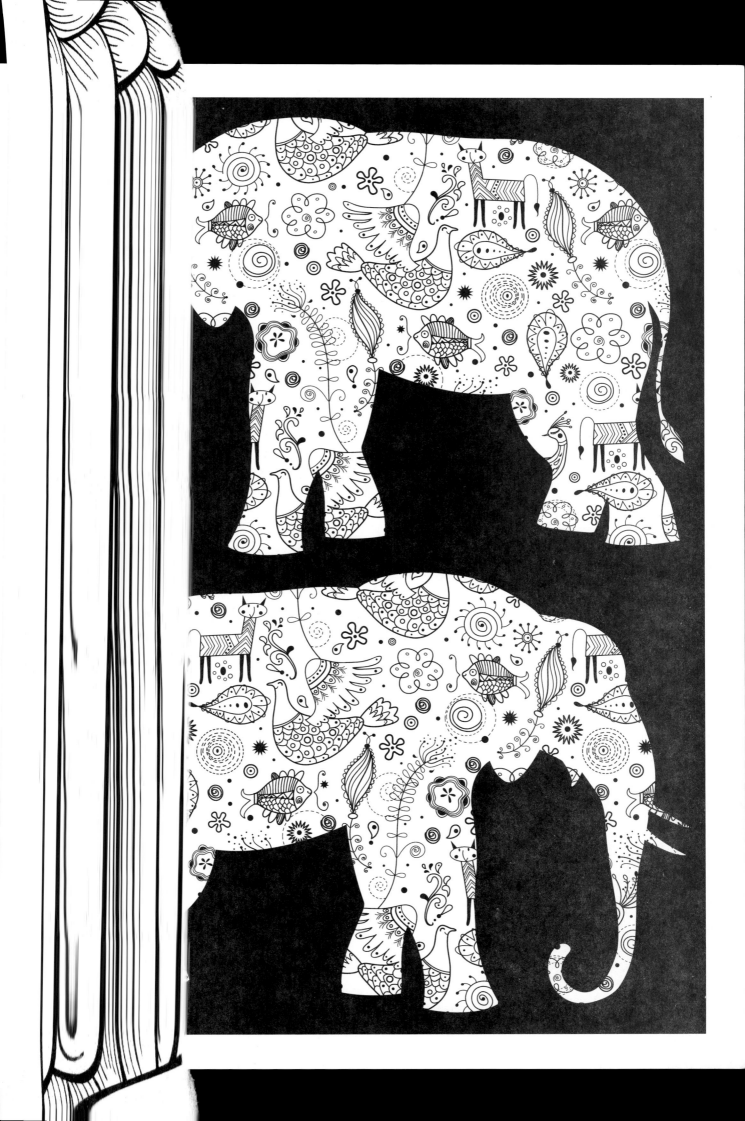

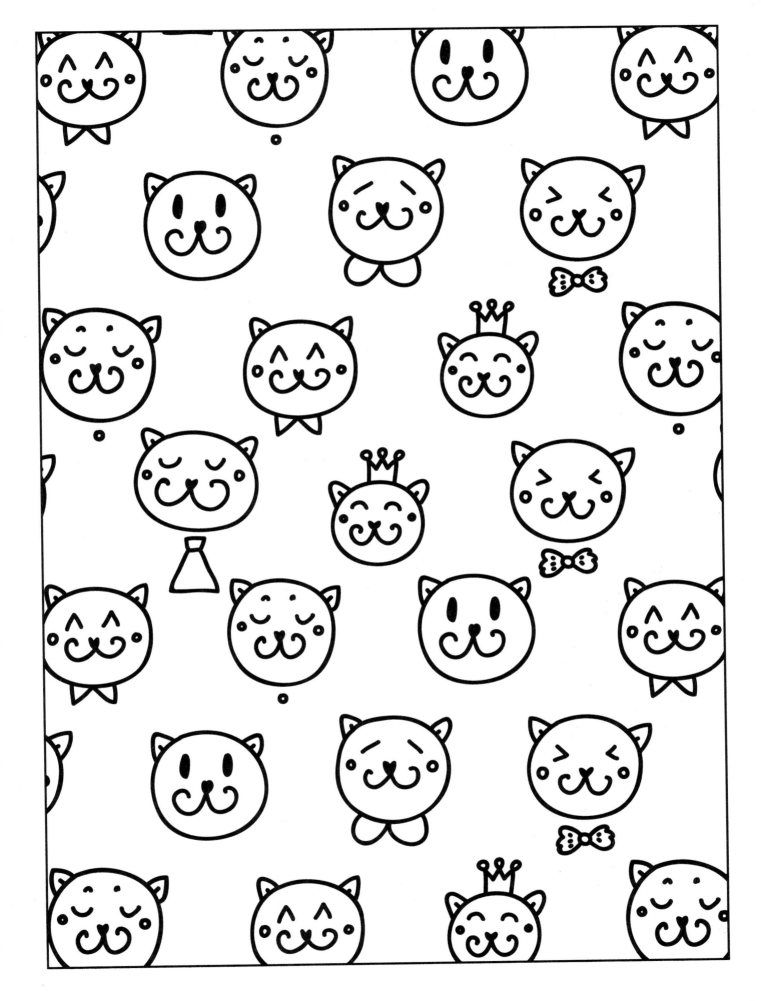

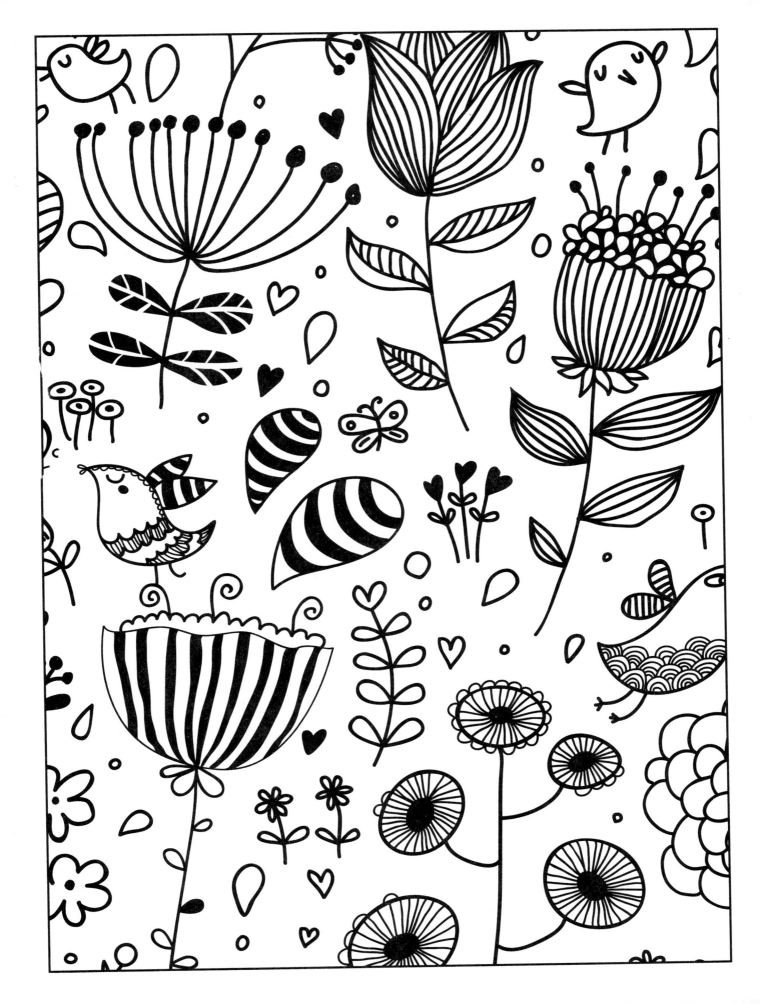

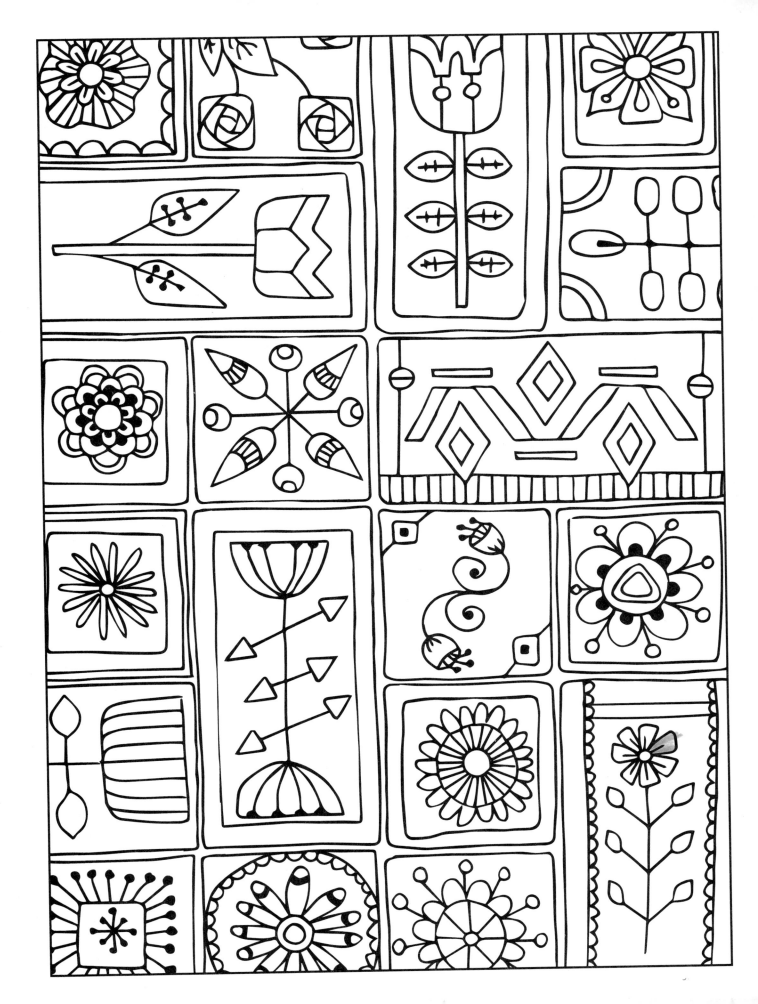

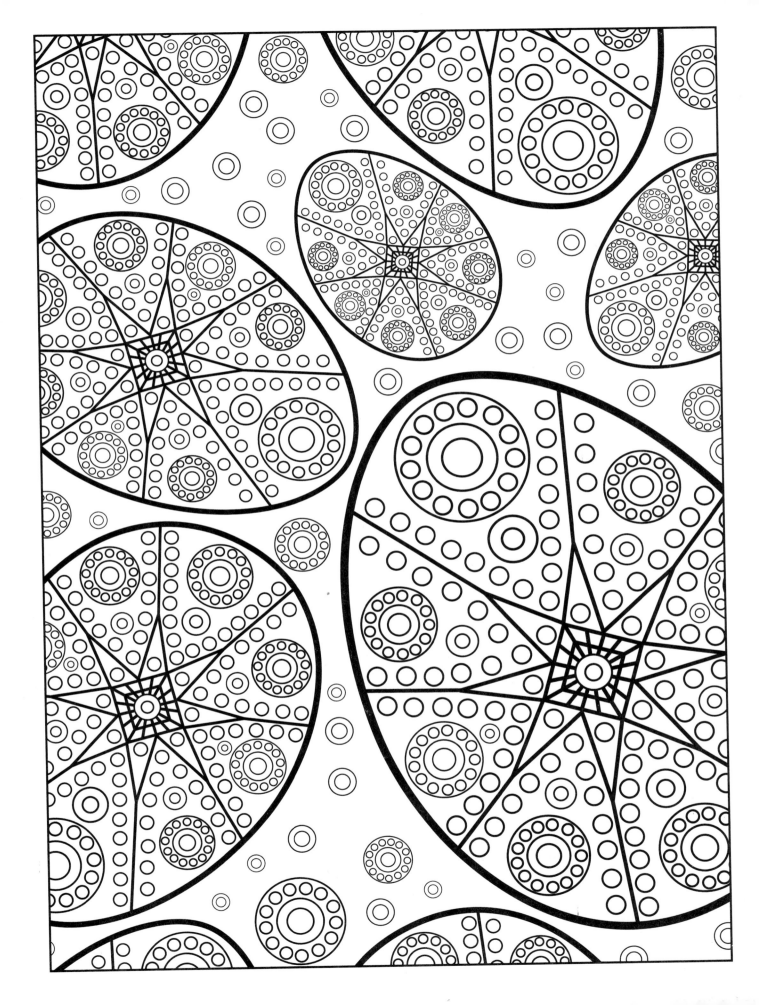

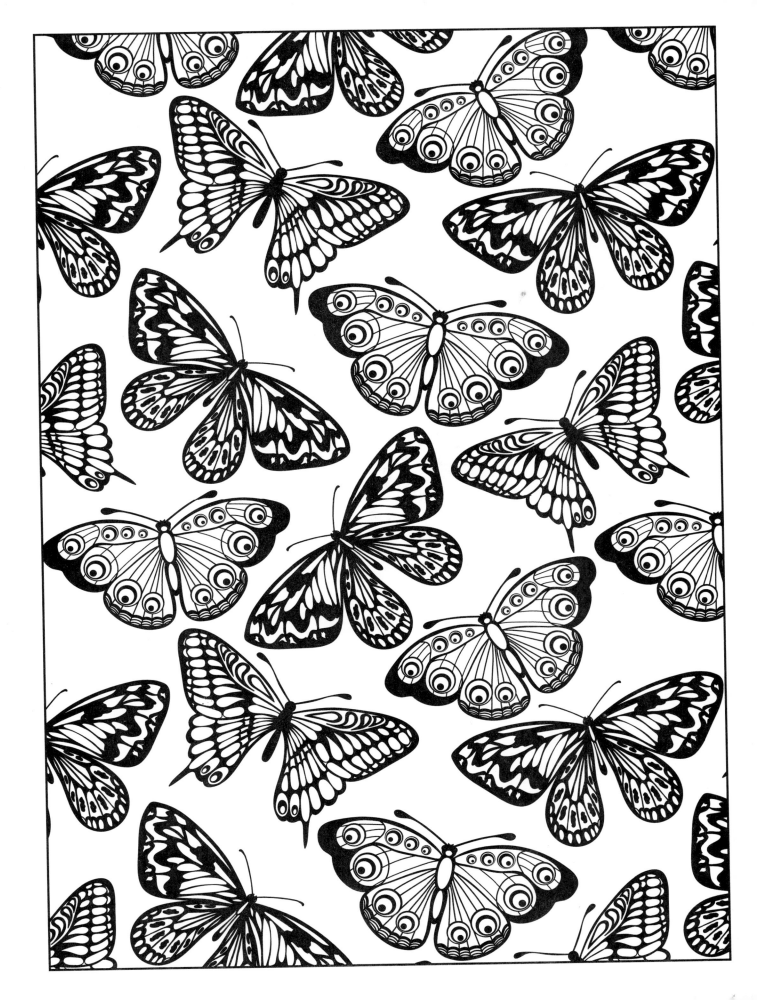

Brooke ♥

Boragah

Brooke

Boragah

Brooke

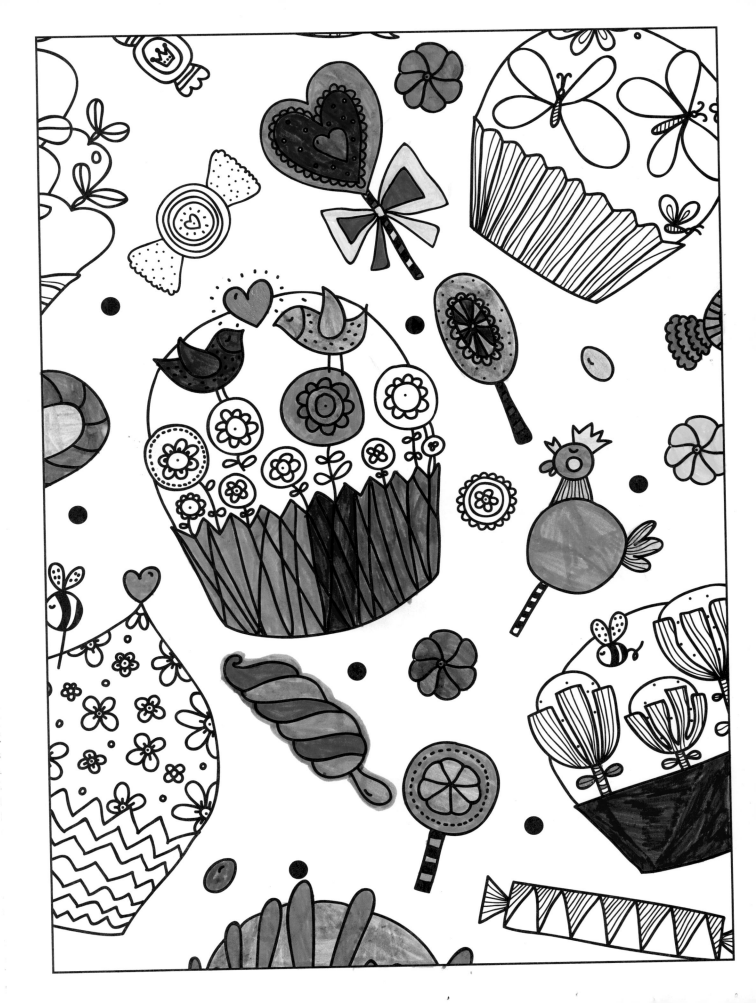

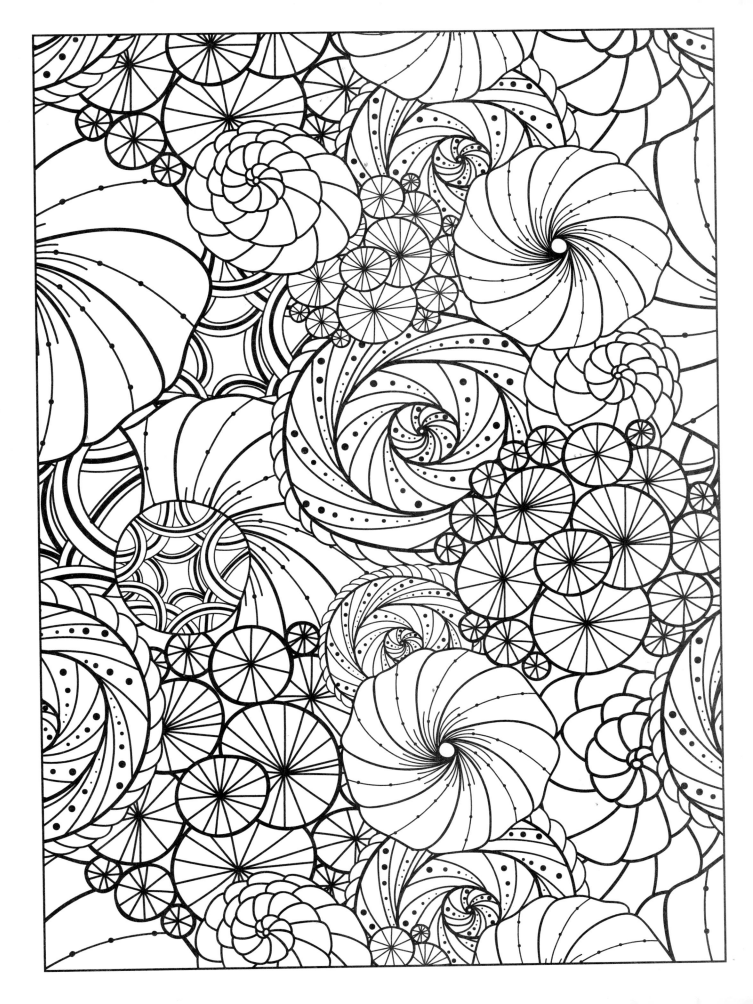

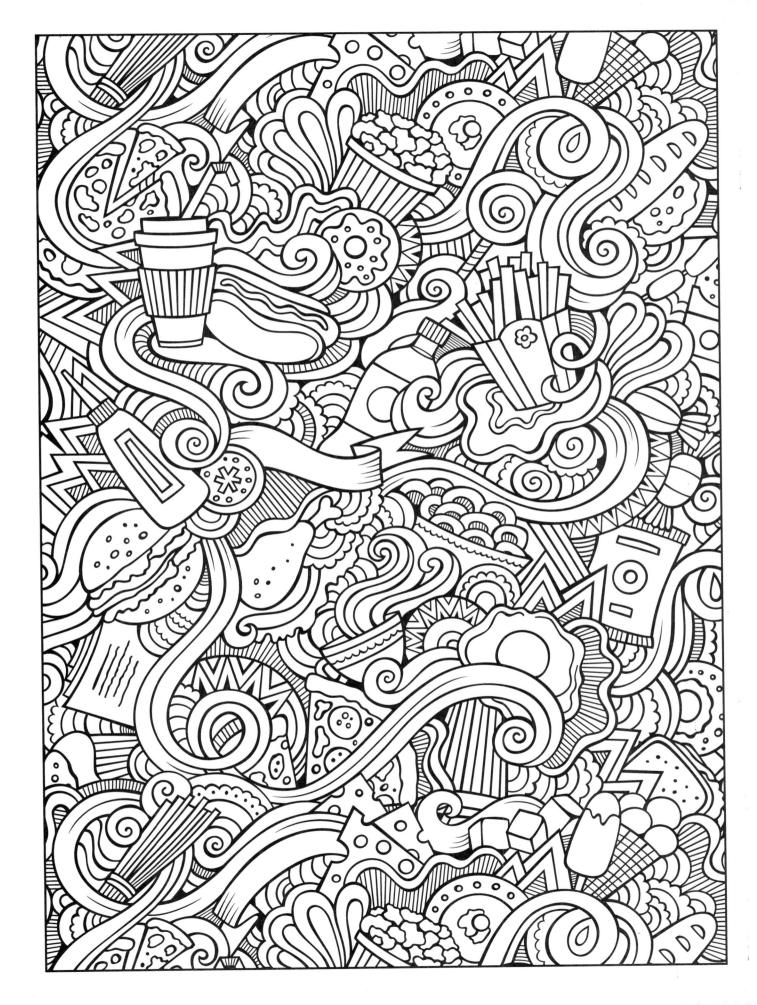

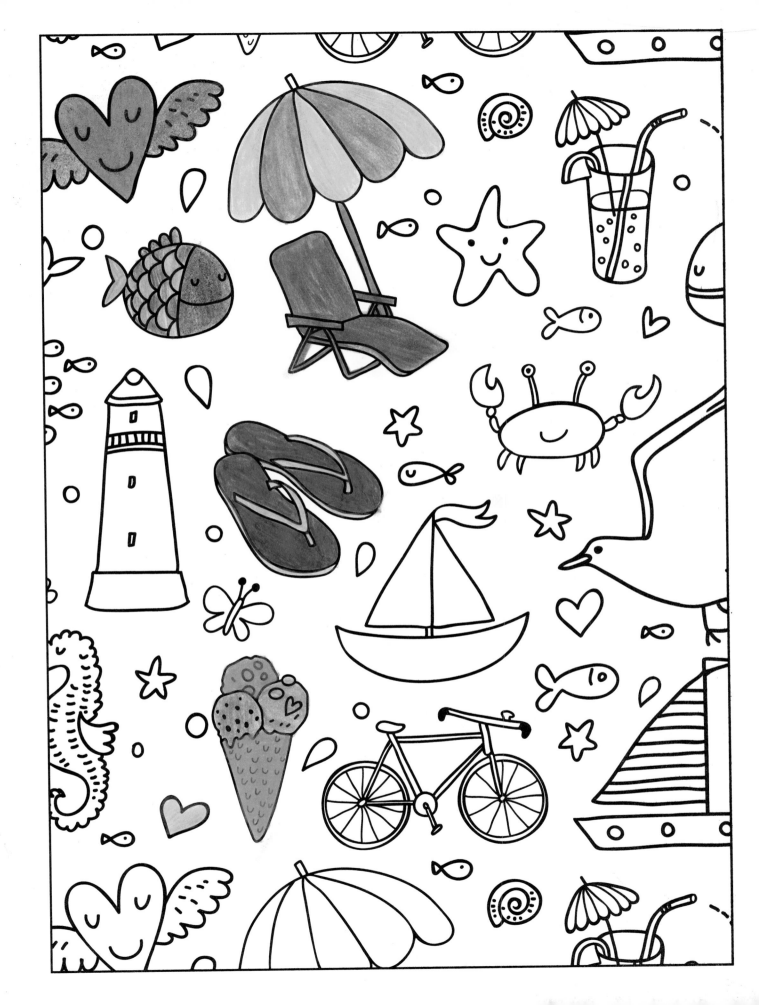

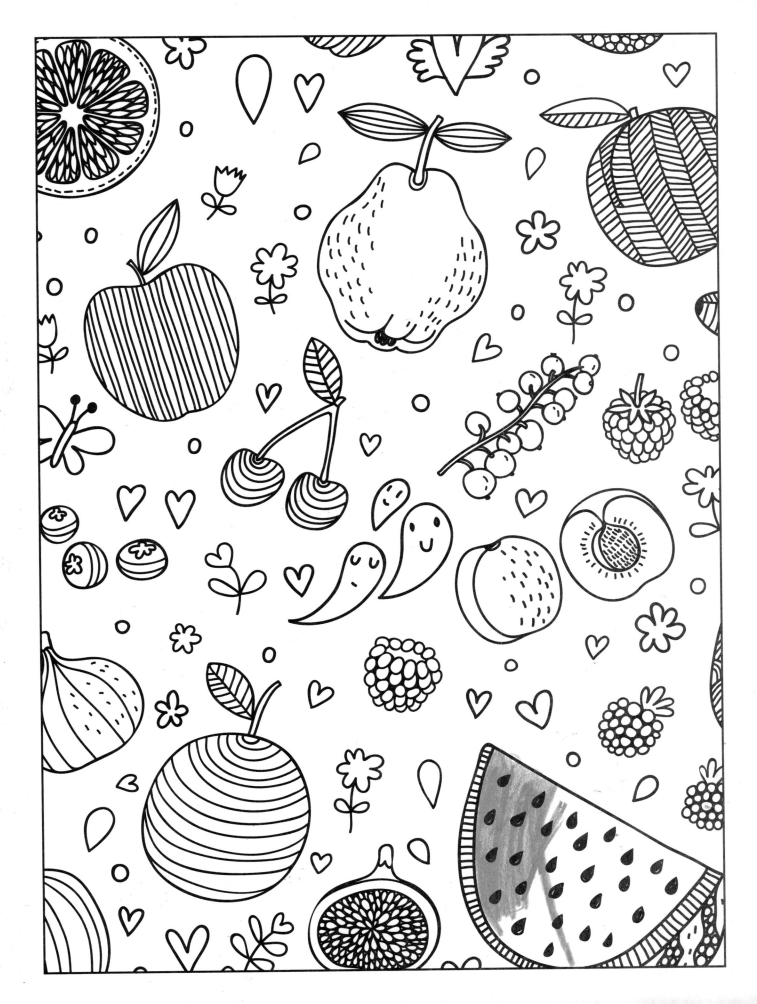

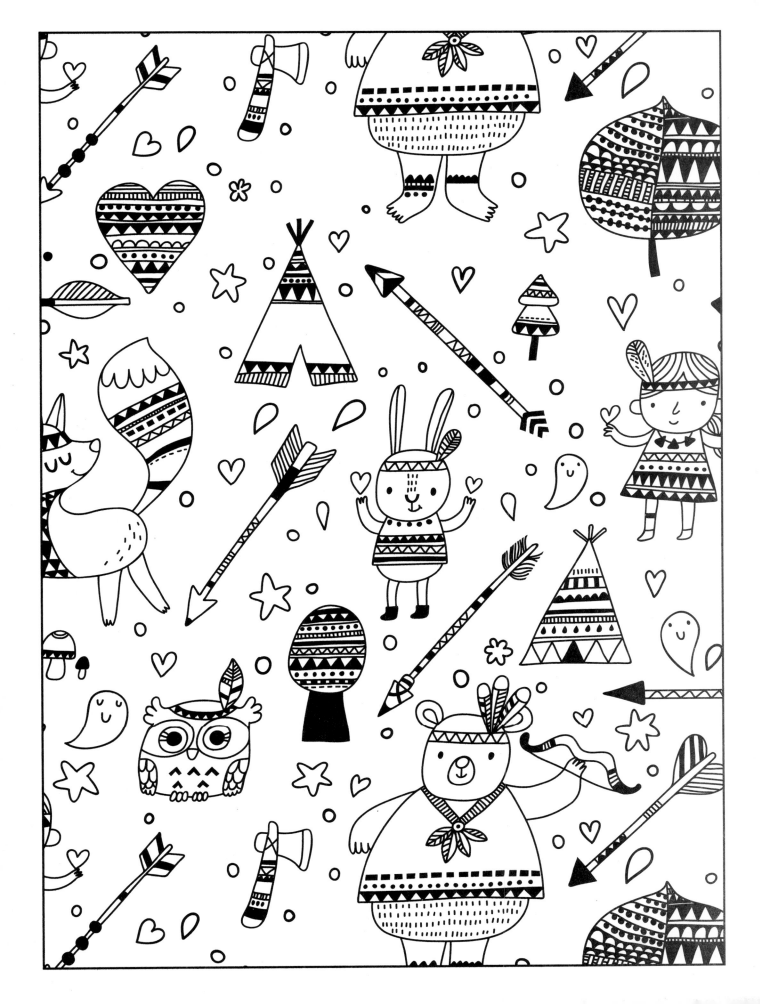

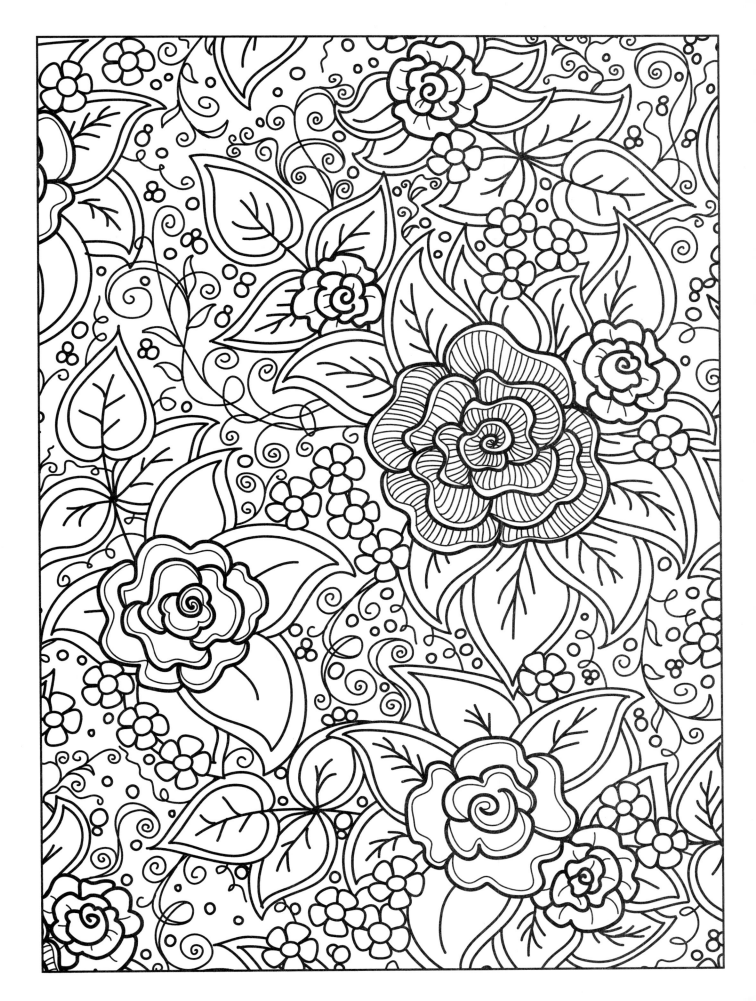

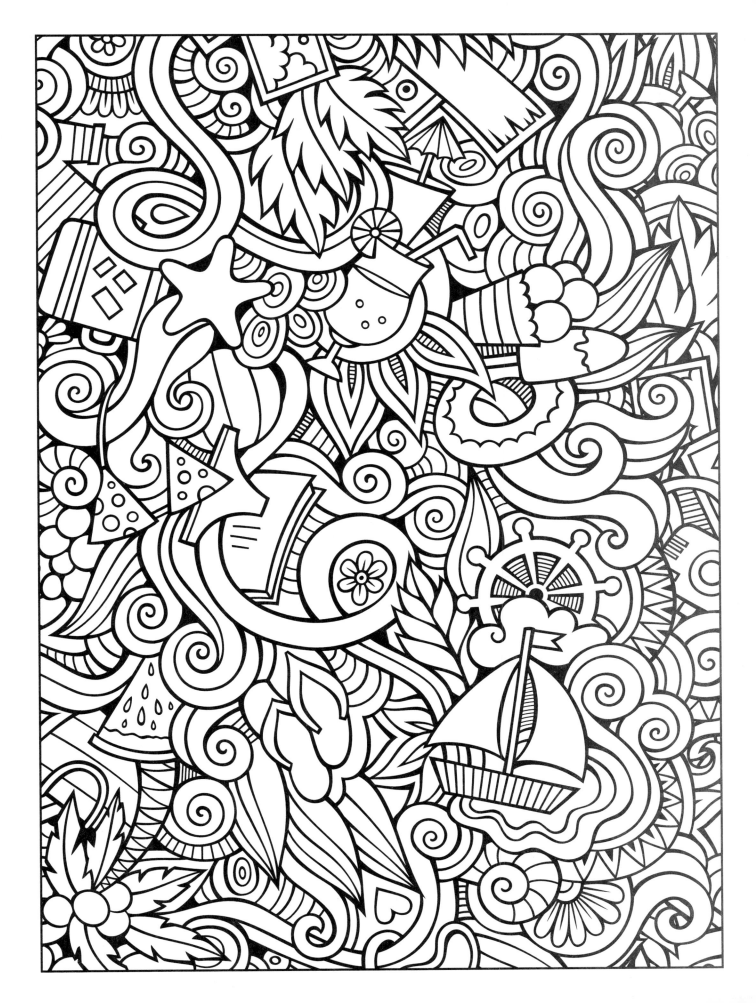

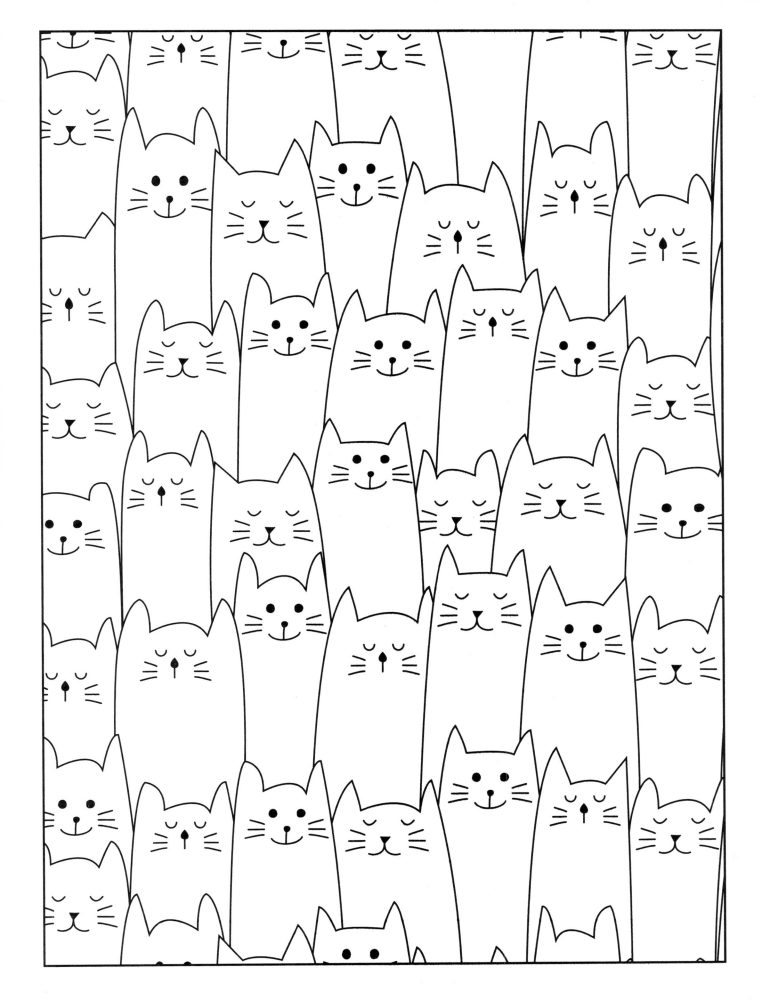

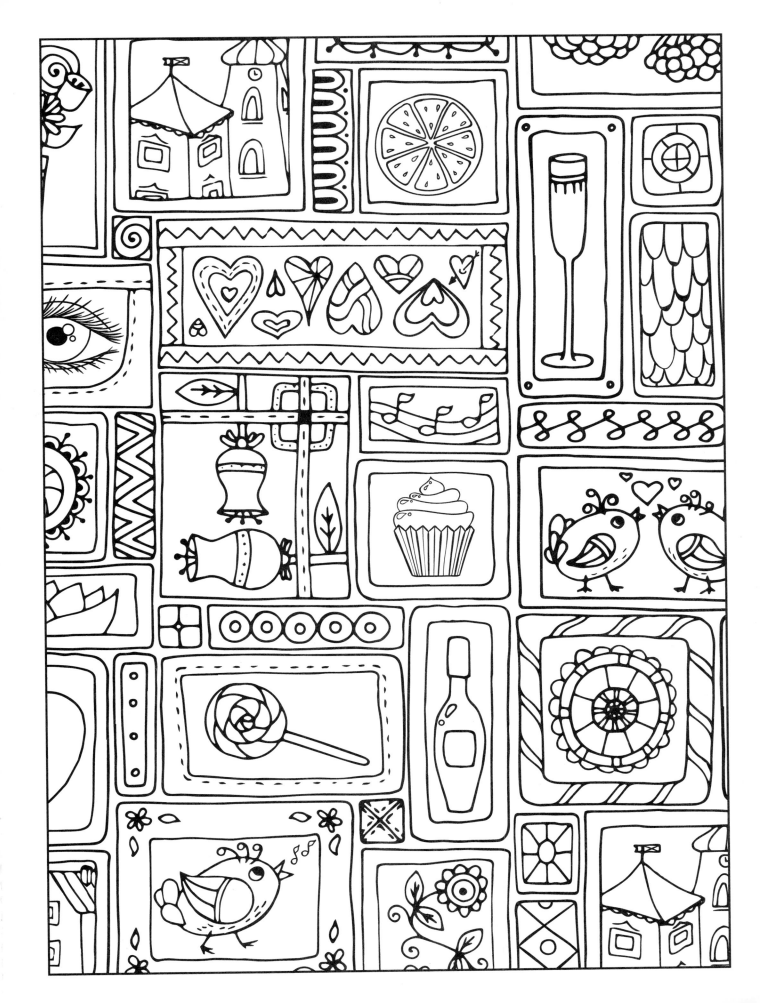

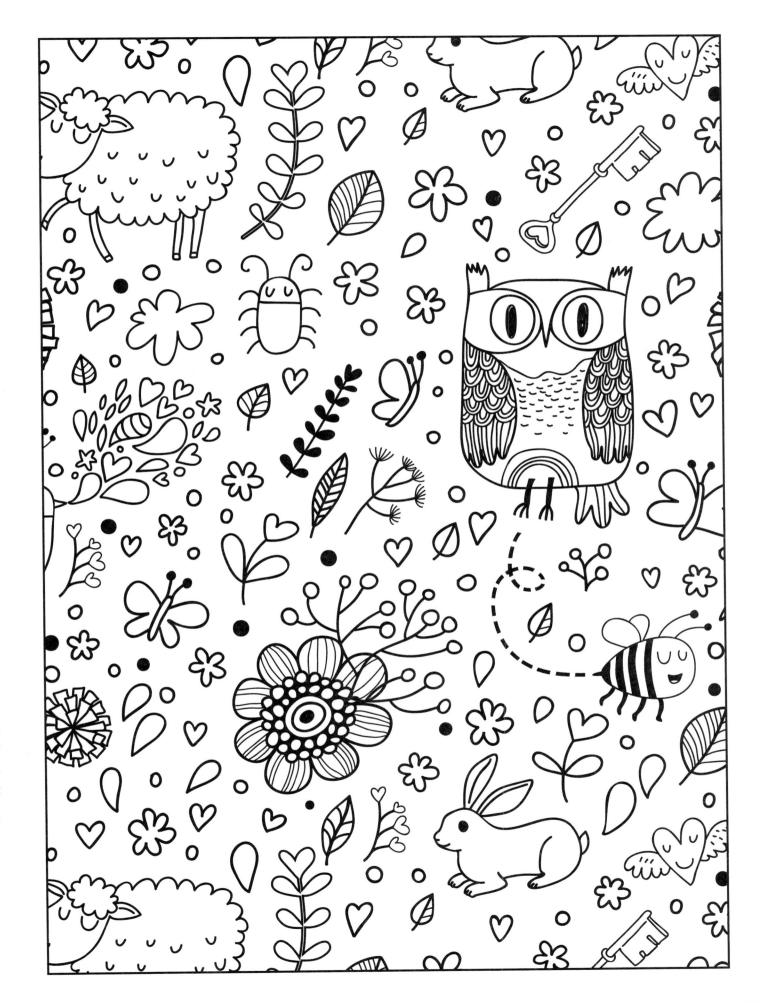

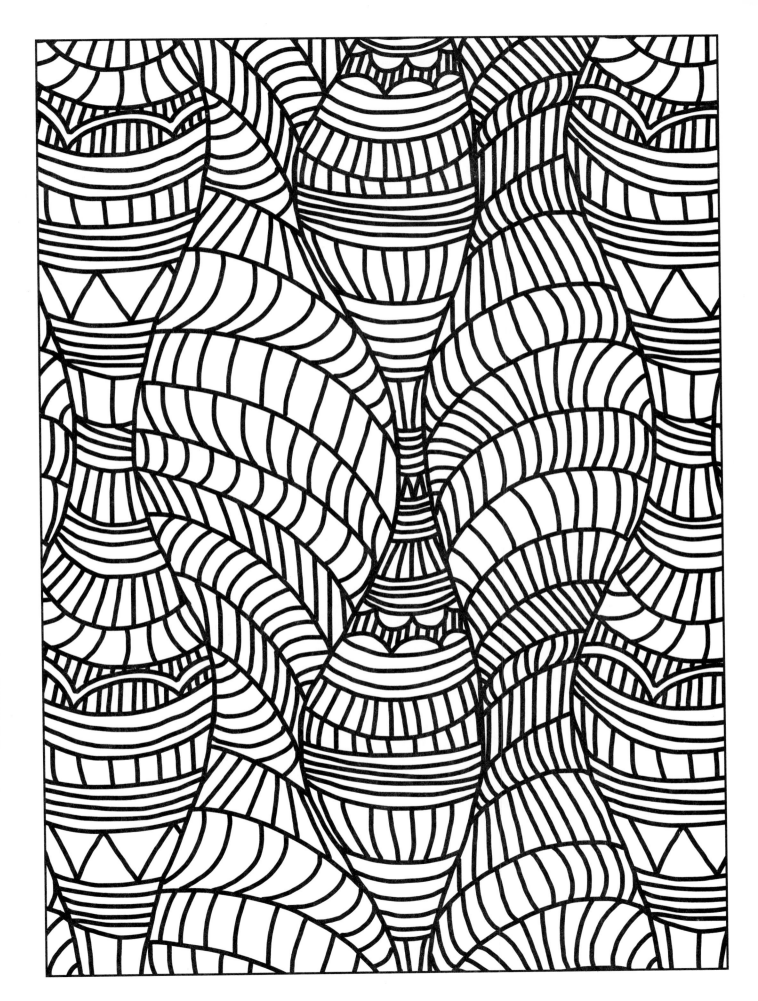

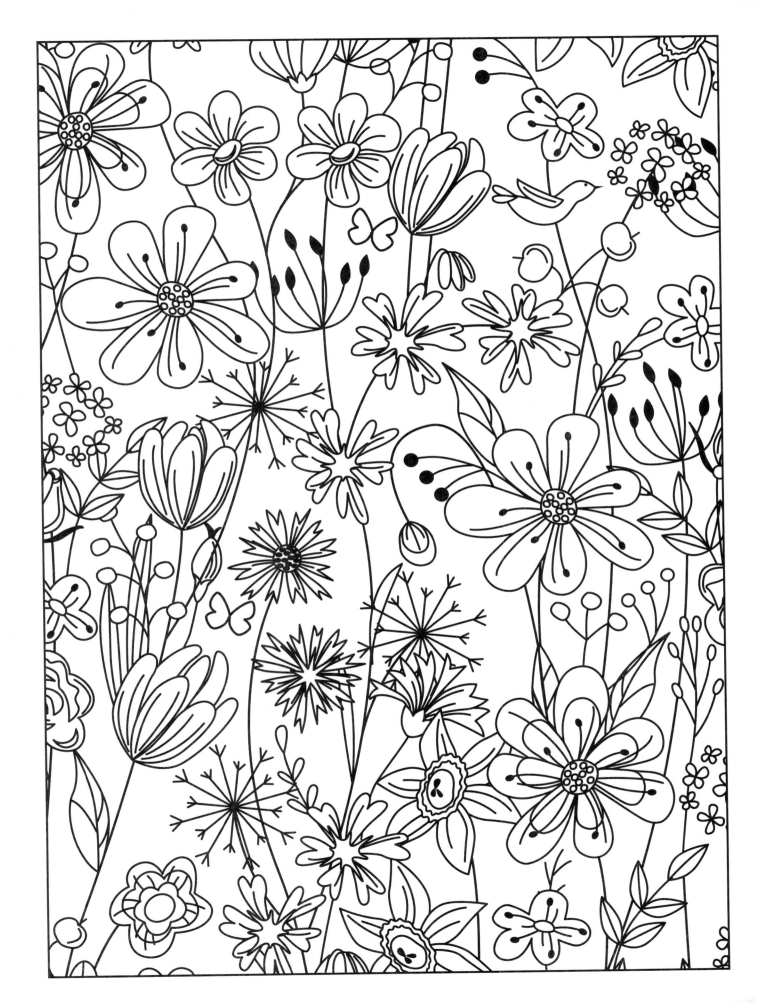

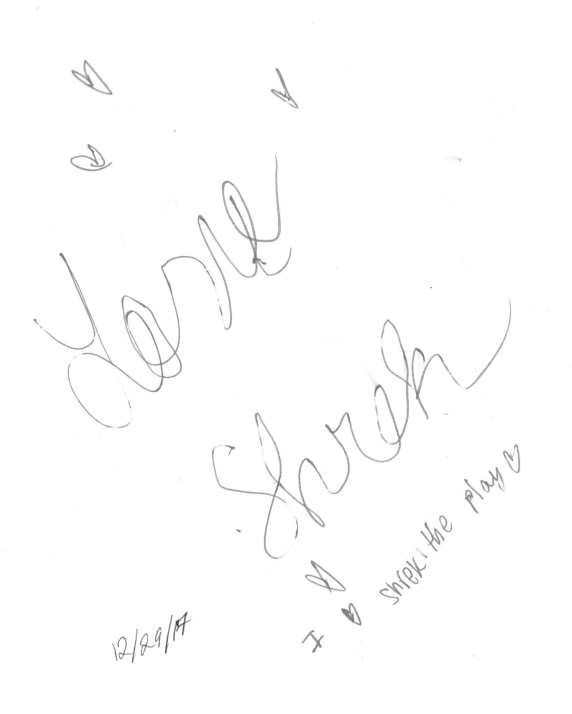

Love

Shrek

12/29/17

I ♡ shrek the play ♡

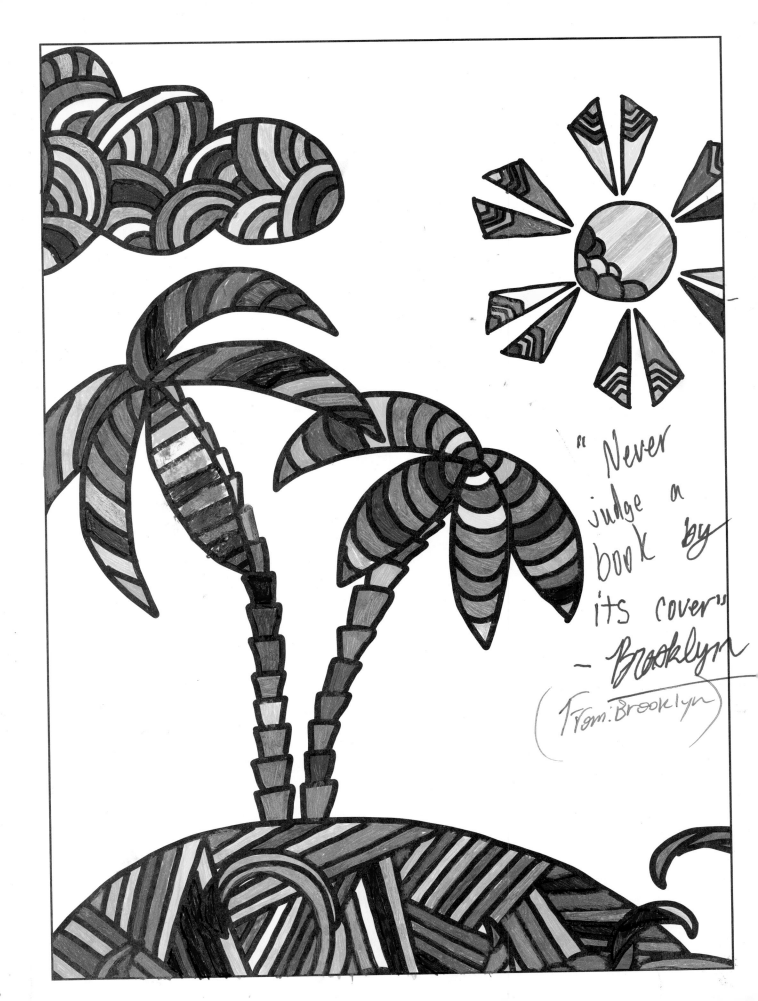

"Never judge a book by its cover"
— Brooklyn

(From: Brooklyn)

12/28/17

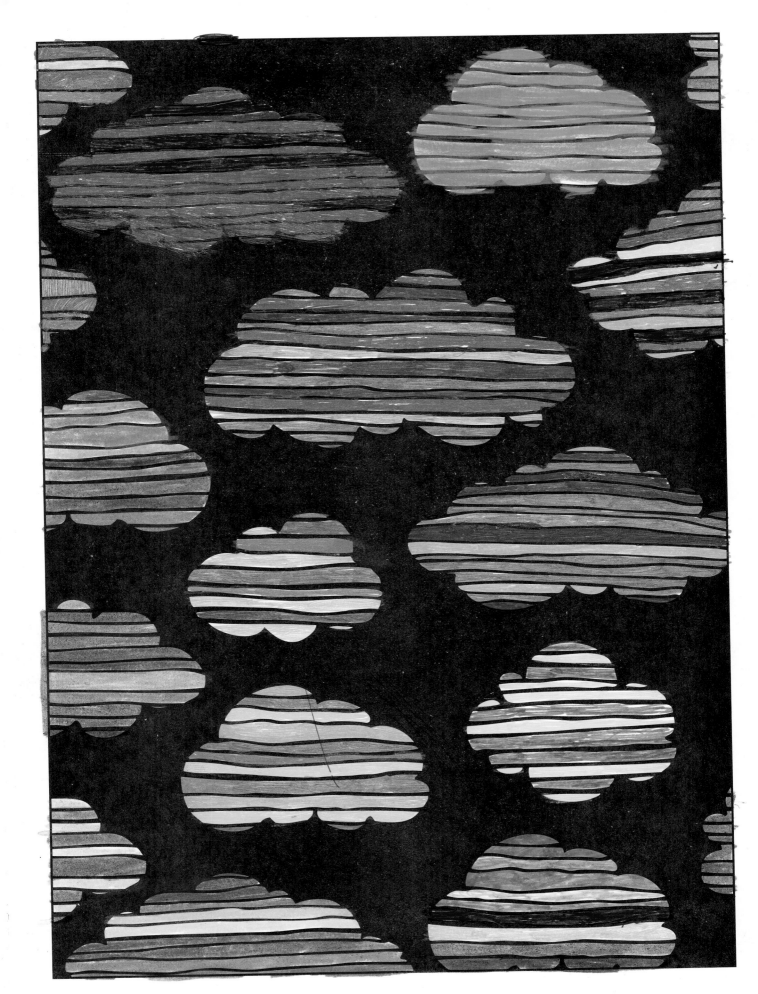

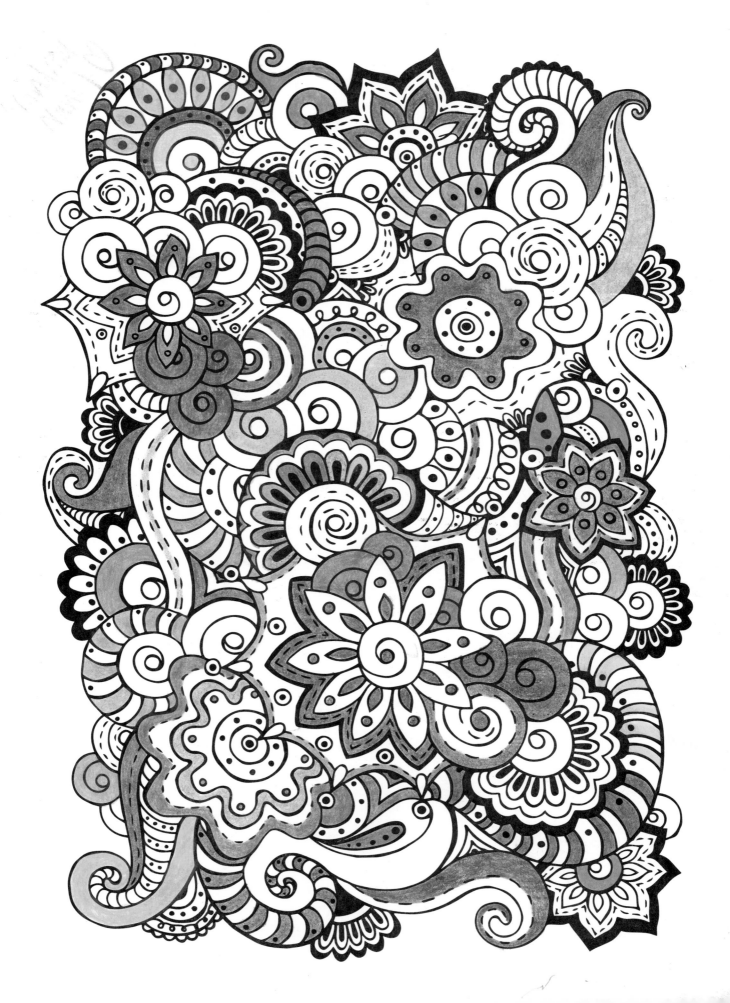

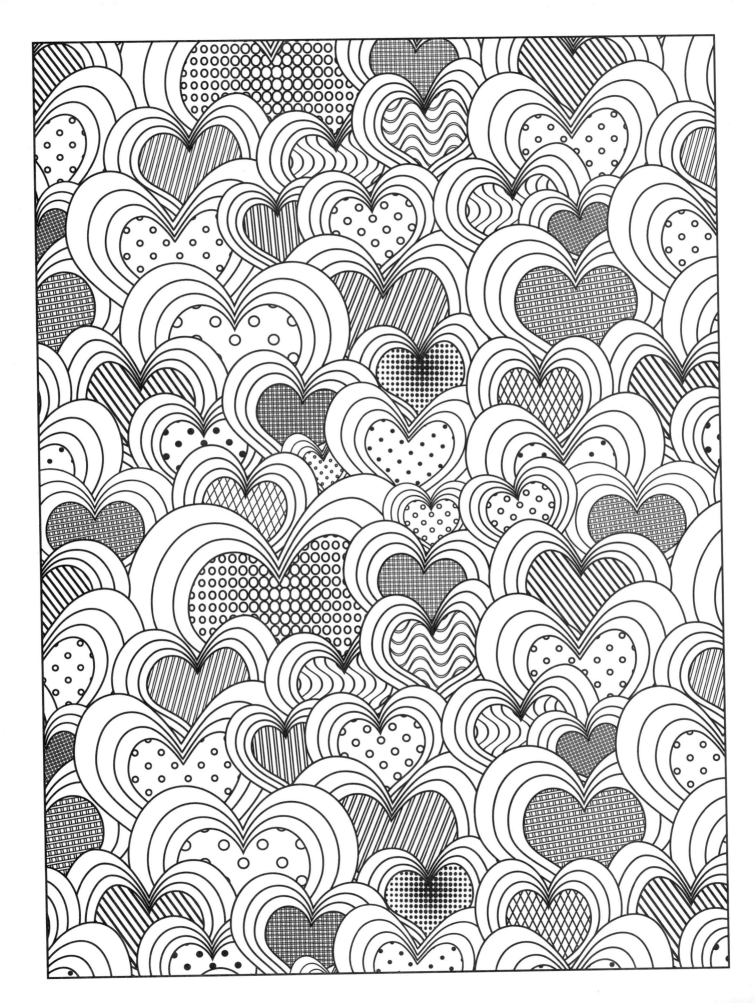

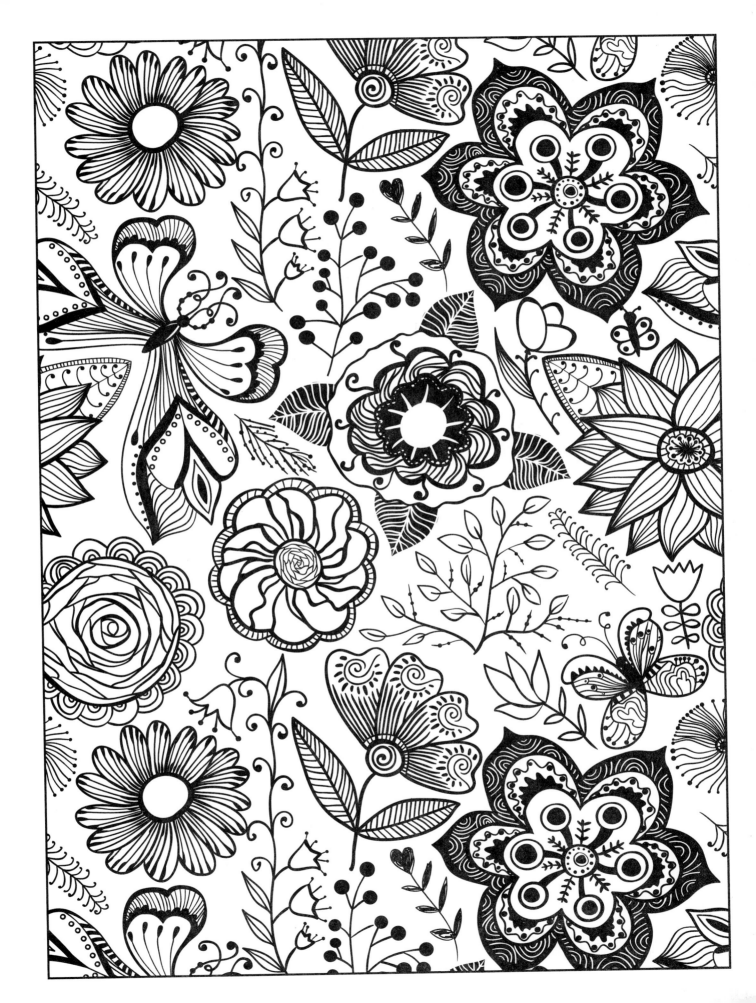

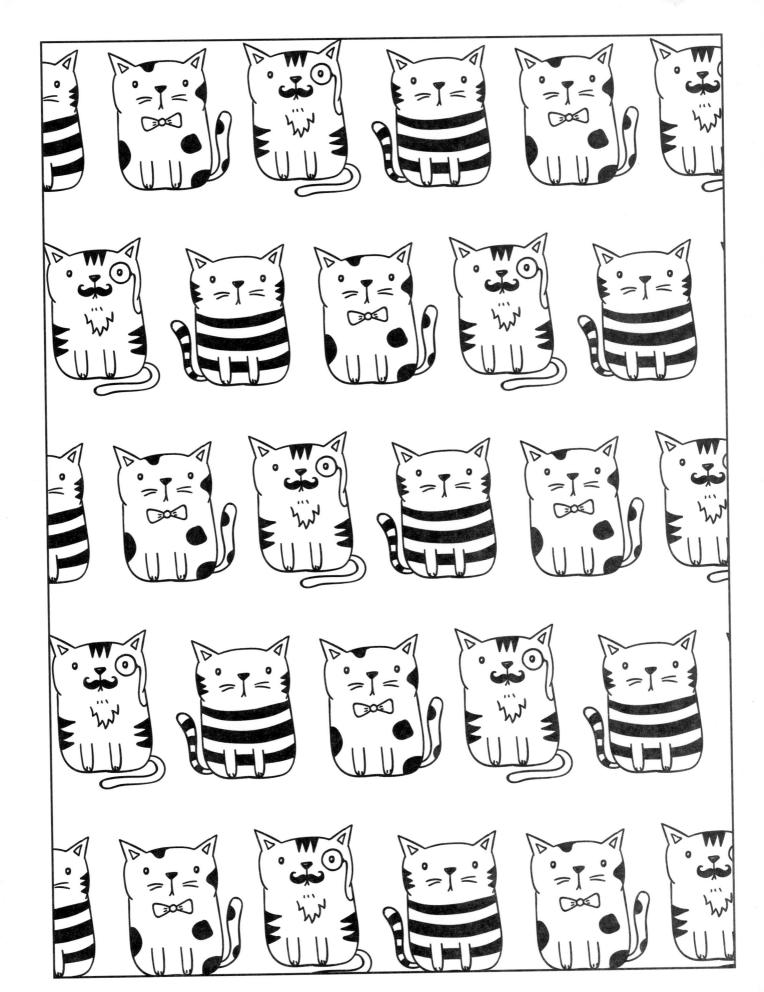

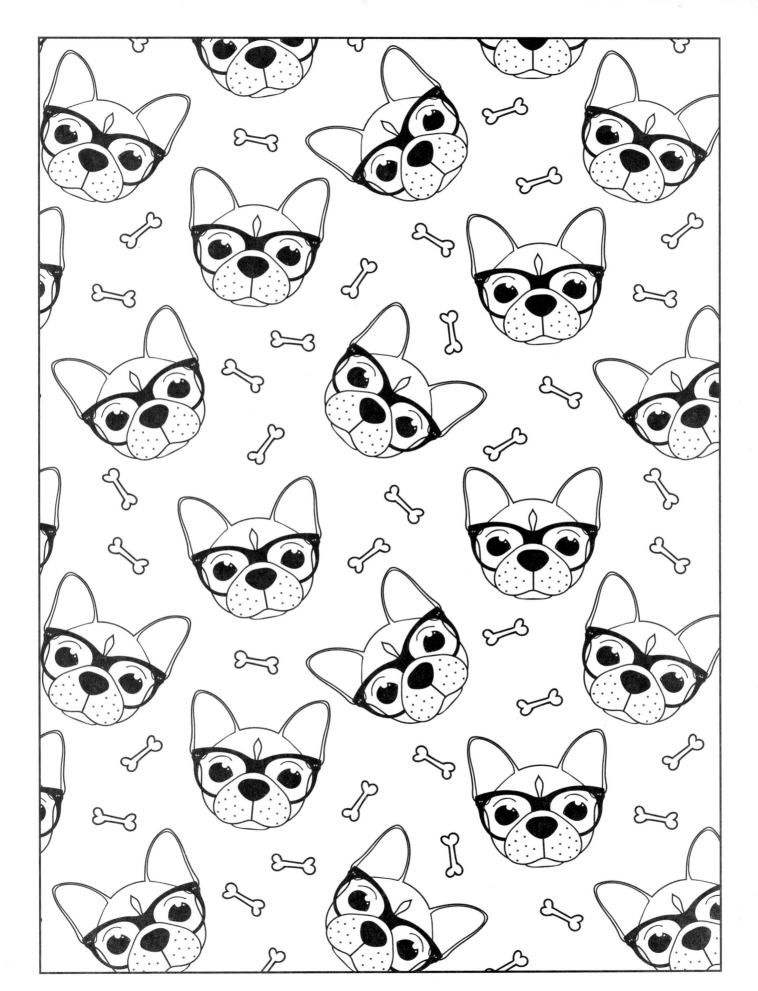

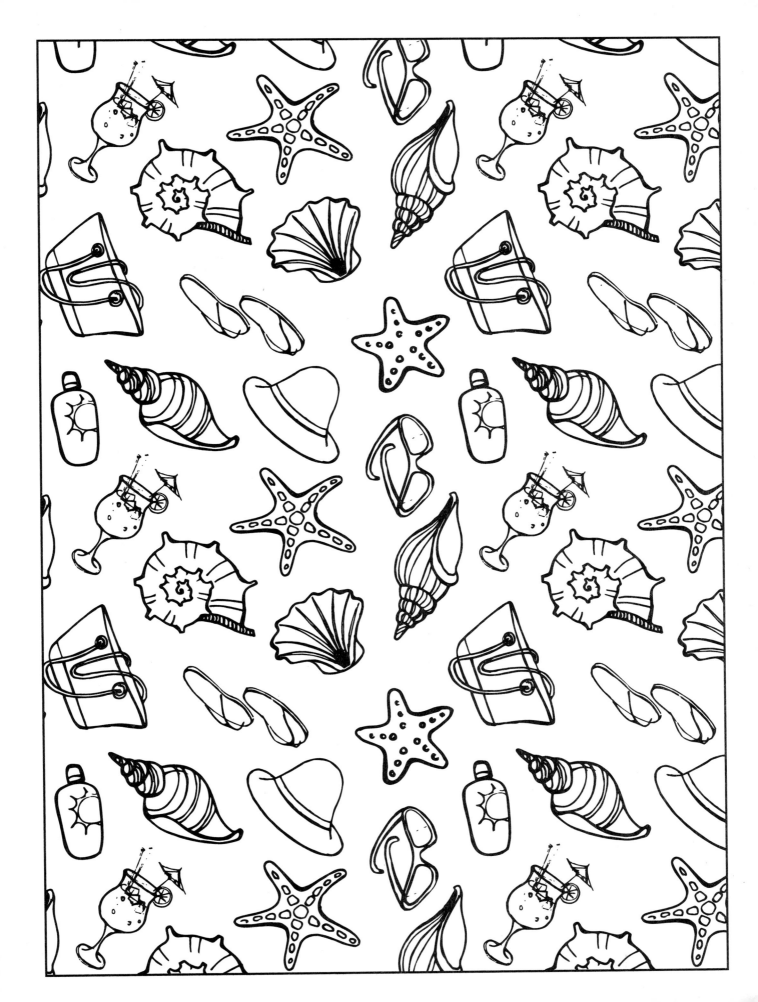

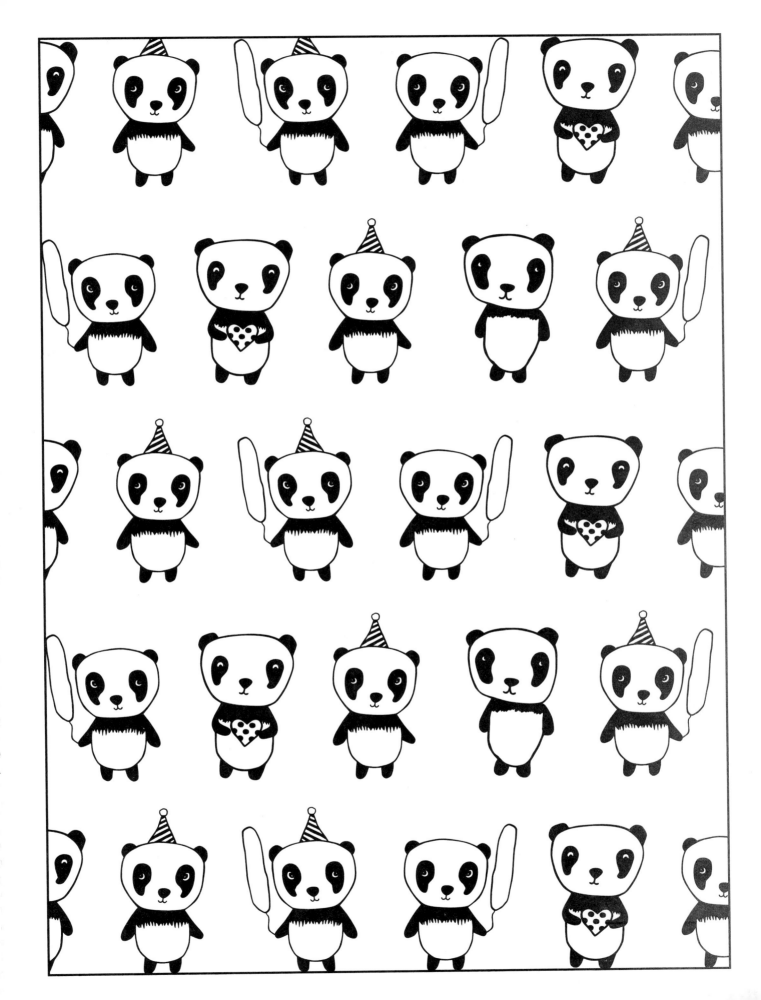

12/29/17